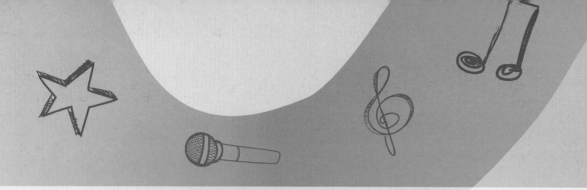

This Annual belongs to

Name ....

Superstar Talent ....

EGMONT
We bring stories to life

First published in Great Britain 2012 by Egmont UK Limited
239 Kensington High Street, London W8 6SA
Written by Jenny Bak, Lizzie Catford and Beth Harwood. Designed by Andrea Pollock.

'Stage Fighting', based on the episode "Stage Fighting", written By George Doty IV. Based on the Television Series "Victorious", created By Dan Schneider.
'Act Out!', based on the episode "The Great Ping-Pong Scam", written By Matt Fleckenstein. Based on the Television Series "Victorious", created By Dan Schneider.
'Jade Dumps Beck', based on the episode "Jade Dumps Beck", written By Matt Fleckenstein. Based on the Television Series "Victorious", created By Dan Schneider.

ISBN 978 1 4052 6431 0
52970/1
Printed in Italy

Contents

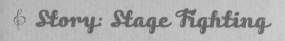

The Lowdown

Tori Vega has always lived in the shadow of her sister, Trina, so she never thought she had a shot at a top stage school like **Hollywood Arts.**

But when she's forced to step into Trina's role in the school's singing showcase, everyone is wowed by Tori's **superstar talent!**

Straight away, Tori is accepted into Hollywood Arts, and that's when the **drama** really kicks in. It's never easy being the new girl at school ... but with her big dreams, gorgeous style and amazing voice, **Tori totally shines!**

Go Hollywood!

HOLLYWOOD ARTS HIGH SCHOOL

Hollywood Arts is one of the **best** stage schools in California. All the students – except Tori! – have to audition their special talents to be accepted. What's the **star-making** talent that would get **you** into HA?

Fill out this school application, and be sure to talk yourself up, **Trina-style!**

Hollywood Arts Application Form

Name: _____

Stage name: _____

What kind of star would you like to be? Tick all that apply.

☐ Singer ☐ Dancer ☐ Actor ☐ Musician ☐ Artist ☐ Songwriter

☐ Other: _____

Have you performed in front of anyone? Where and when?

_____

Describe your style: _____

_____

Likes: _____

_____

Hates: _____

_____

Your three-word bio: _____ _____ _____

Why do you want to attend Hollywood Arts High School?

_____

_____

Hollywood Arts values individuality in our students. Decorate this form any way you like so we can see your personality shine through!

Tori

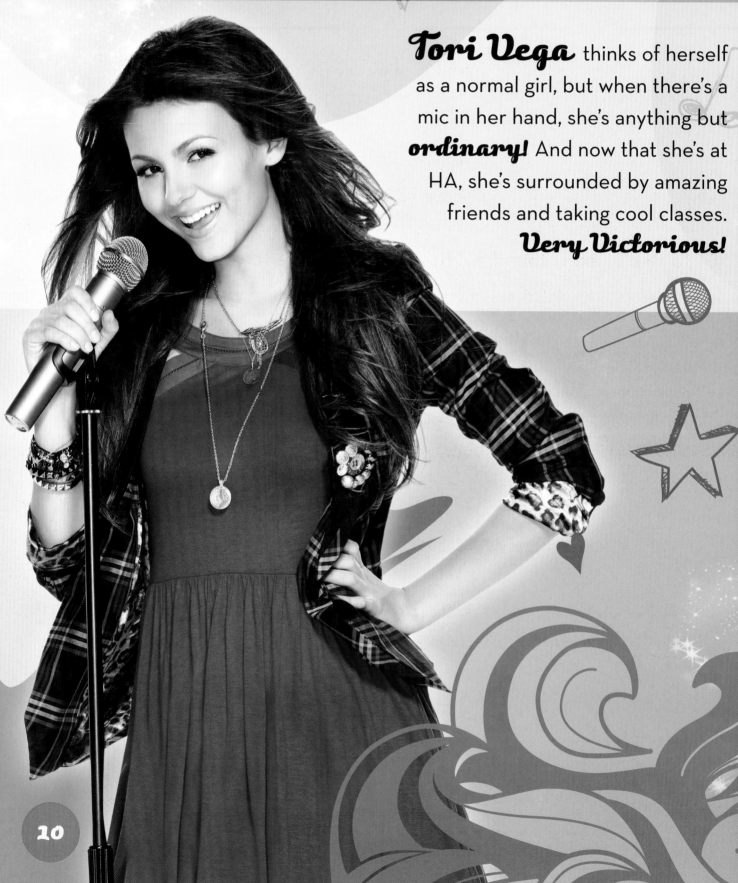

Tori Vega thinks of herself as a normal girl, but when there's a mic in her hand, she's anything but **ordinary!** And now that she's at HA, she's surrounded by amazing friends and taking cool classes. **Very Victorious!**

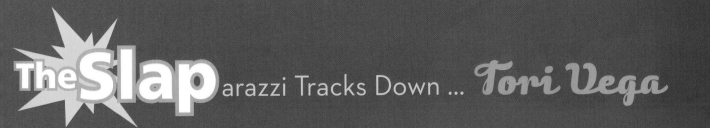

The Slaparazzi Tracks Down ... *Tori Vega*

The Slap It's impossible to get into ***Hollywood Arts High School***. How did you do it?

Tori: This is going to sound crazy, but it's all thanks to a Chinese herb gargle. After Trina gargled this weird herb to improve her voice, her tongue swelled up so much that she couldn't sing in HA's Big Showcase. Andre forced me to step in, and I found out how much I love performing. And that's when the principal asked me to enrol!

The Slap Trina can be a bit ... er ... ***'high maintenance'***. How do you deal?

Tori: Trina definitely loves to be the centre of attention, but she's also friendly, fun and a super-supportive big sis.

The Slap Who's your bestie?

Tori: I've made some fantastic friends at school, but Andre is definitely numero uno! He's always believed in me, even when *I* didn't. That's what you call a good pal.

The Slap So where do you see yourself in ten years?

Tori: That's no secret ... My big dream is to be a successful pop star doing what I love – ***singing!***

11

Andre

Andre Harris is an awesome musician, singer and songwriter ... he even wrote the brilliant song that brought Tori to HA, **"Make it Shine"**. He's funny, laidback and sweet – everything Tori could want in a **BFF!**

The Slap Three things you can't live without?

Andre: My keyboard. Inside-out burgers. My PearPhone. And my grandma!

The Slap That's four, but we'll let it go cos the last one was so sweet! Who are you crushing on right now?

Andre: Er ... uh ... um ... No comment?

The Slap Can you give us a hint?

Andre: Let's just say she's got an amazing voice that she should use for singing, not making threats.

The Slap Fast forward ten years. What will you be doing?

Andre: Playing my triple-platinum hit songs to a sold-out arena audience. Nothing too ambitious!

12

Trina

Trina Vega is just a year older than Tori, but the two sisters are as different as chalk and cheese. Trina is convinced – or **deluded** – that her undeniable looks and talent will blast her into **superstardom** one day, even if no one else agrees!

TheSlap You've been at HA awhile ... any words of wisdom for new pupils?

Trina: They should get my autograph now while they can ... it'll be worth a LOT of money soon.

TheSlap What do you consider your best feature?

Trina: Me. You can't break down perfection.

TheSlap What's the best thing about having your sister at HA?

Trina: I love that Tori's so talented! Plus, she carries my bag home so I don't ruin my manicure.

Beck

Beck Oliver, with his laidback attitude and wicked surfing skills, is a *California boy* through and through. And although there are some serious sparks between him and Tori, Beck would never do anything to hurt his girlfriend, Jade. Another reason why *he's so dreamy!*

The Slap How do you get your hair so pretty?

Beck: It's a secret I'll take to my grave. And in that grave, you'll find some hair gel.

The Slap Is it true that Jade once shouted at a girl for feeling your hair?

Beck: Have you met Jade? Enough said.

The Slap So if acting doesn't work out, what's the backup plan?

Beck: Probably working at a funeral home with Jade. Wait, will she see this? Just a joke, schnookums!

The Slap Romantic! Who has the better voice – Jade or Tori? It'll be our little secret.

Beck: I'd like to live long enough to graduate from school, so ... definitely Jade.

Jade

Goth girl **Jade West** has a notorious **mean streak** that has most everyone at Hollywood Arts terrified, especially anyone who dares flirt with her boyfriend, Beck.

TheSlap You're a triple threat – singer, actress and playwright. Tell us about the last play you wrote.

Jade: It's a horror story about a high school website that poisons everyone who visits it. It's called *TheSlap.com*.

TheSlap Moving right along ... you and Beck have been dating for two years. What's the nicest thing you've done for him?

Jade: I protect him from the pathetic girls who think they can charm him away from me. I teach them otherwise.

TheSlap Scary! Rumour has it that you got him a puppy. Awww!

Jade: It was actually a Rottweiler that ended up sending his dad to hospital.

TheSlap Um ... one more question. What's in your bag?

Jade: Scissors, very *sharp* scissors.

15

Robbie & Rex

Wherever you find **Robbie Shapiro,** you'll also find his friend, **Rex Powers.** Robbie isn't the most confident boy at Hollywood Arts, but Rex makes up for it with his **brutal honesty,** which can be good or really, really bad.

The Slap What's with the dummy?

Rex: Who are you calling a dummy, dummy?
Robbie: I'm sure they didn't mean anything bad by that.
Rex: No one asked you!

The Slap Sorry. Let's start over. We hear that Rex has a packed social life. How about you, Robbie?

Robbie: I'm really busy. Tonight I'm playing video games. Tomorrow I'm playing video games. I'm not sure about the weekend, but it might involve some video games.
Rex: I've got a date with two girls tonight.
Robbie: Ooh, can I come?
Rex: Have you got any money?
Robbie: You took all of it already.
Rex: In that case ... no.

Cat

Sweet and silly **Cat Valentine** is the first girl that Tori becomes friends with at Hollywood Arts. She's an **awesome** singer and actress, and a lot smarter than she lets on. Cat might blurt out the most **random** things at the most random times, but hey ... **she's never boring!**

TheSlap Did you dye your hair red because your surname is Valentine?

Cat: What's *that* supposed to mean?!

TheSlap Er, because valentines are red?

Cat: Oh. It's because I love red velvet cupcakes.

TheSlap Right. What's your favourite song?

Cat: Did you know my brother once broke his tailbone? I didn't even know he had a tail!

TheSlap Oooooookay ... and the song?

Cat: Or that it had a bone in it.

TheSlap It's not really a — never mind. Interview done.

Cat: Yay! Do I get a prize?

TheSlap ARGH!

Stage Fighting

Techniques of Acting was one of Tori's favourite classes. She was especially excited for today's lesson – her teacher, Liam, was showing them how to stage fight, which was **fake fighting** for movies and plays.

As the class watched, Liam demonstrated ways to appear as if he were giving and taking blows that looked way too real ... and painful. Tori couldn't **wait** to try it!

"All right!" Liam called to the class when he had finished. "I'll pair you up so you can prepare a fight scene to show us on Wednesday."

"Awesome!" Tori beamed at Andre. But the smile was quickly wiped off her face when Liam announced that her partner was going to be **Jade**. Tori's heart sank. The **Queen of Mean** had shouted at her at lunchtime for talking to Beck, and Tori was still recovering from the trauma.

"Hi, Tori." Jade had slipped up next to her. "I can't wait for our fight. *Scene*, that is."

Jade's Look of Doom

With a **sinking** feeling, Tori thought to herself, *this is not going to end well.*

Nowhere to hide!

By Wednesday, Tori was **terrified**. She and Jade had practiced their fight scene a few times without any problems, but Tori wasn't fooled. *Jade's waiting until class to hit me*, she thought as she plodded to class. *Just to* **humiliate** *me in front of everyone.*

As pair after pair of her classmates did their realistic-looking fight scenes, Tori's **fear** grew. When it was her turn, she put on her old-lady costume, complete with grey wig and cane, and stepped miserably into place. As their scene began, Tori shuffled across the stage until she felt a hand **grabbing** her shoulder from behind.

"Gimme your money and your watch!" shouted Jade, easily playing the part of a violent mugger.

Bad hair day for Tori

In her best old-lady voice, Tori croaked, "Wouldn't you rather have *this*?" and spun around, **swinging** her cane at the robber. Liam played the *CRACK!* sound effect that made the blow sound sickeningly **real.**

"Ow!" Jade dropped to the floor with a **thud**, holding her hand to her face. A thin line of red seeped through her fingers. "She hit my eye!"

Beck rushed over. "Are you OK?" he asked, worried.

"No! She hit me in the face for *real*," **gasped** Jade.

Ouch – that looks painful!

"No, I didn't!" Tori said, shocked.

"Tell that to my eye!" shouted Jade, showing the **bloody** gash.

Andre pulled Tori aside. "Why did you hit her?" he asked soberly.

Andre confronts Tori

"I didn't!" Tori insisted. Even her best friend didn't believe her! She **stormed** over to Jade, who was whinging pathetically to the concerned crowd around her. "You know I didn't hit you. I swung but I missed, just like we practised."

The damsel in distress

"Ohhh ..." Jade started to **faint**, but was quickly caught by Beck. "Somebody please ... call my mum ..."

As Beck helped her out of the room, Jade glanced mournfully back at Tori. "And I thought we were just starting to be **friends**..."

"But I didn't ..." Tori helplessly tried to explain to her friends, but they had all walked away.

No one believes her!

Tori didn't think it was possible for the next day to be even **worse**, but it was. She was in the middle of maths when she was summoned to see Lane, the guidance counsellor.

Things just keep getting worse ...

"Hi, Tori," Lane said cheerfully. "Don't look so worried. I'm here to help you with your **violence issues**."

Tori leapt up from her chair. *"I'm not violent!"* she shouted.

"I believe you," Lane said nervously.
But he gave a nod to Derrick, the big, **tough-looking** security guard, before turning back to her. "Jade West has a black eye. It's not okay to beat people you don't like with a cane."

"I did not hit Jade!" Tori yelled, and Derrick jumped in fear. "Oh, **relax**," she snapped.

"Could it be that you were under a lot of stress and were worried about Jade hitting you, and in the heat of the moment, you just **snapped** and hit her?" Lane asked.

Tori began to **doubt** what had really happened. Maybe she *did* mean to hit Jade. "If I say yes, can I go?" she asked tiredly.

"Sure. But I'm giving you two weeks' lunch detention," Lane told her. Derrick gave a little cough, and Lane added, "Plus you have to **clean** the theatre after tomorrow's school play. There's a big food fight scene at the end that should keep you busy for awhile."

Tori sighed. *Just perfect.*

When the final bell rang the next day, Andre was waiting at Tori's locker.

"Guess whaaat?" he sang as she approached. "Jade **faked** her black eye! She got smacked by a water balloon and I saw the makeup wash off. She must have used fake blood during class. "

Jade gets rumbled

Tori couldn't **believe** it ... she knew she hadn't hit Jade! She felt a surge of **anger**. Not only did the whole school think she had violence issues, but she was being **punished** for something she didn't do.

"Thanks for telling me, Andre," she said. "I've got something to do." With **grim** determination, Tori strode off.

TORI VEGA Um, whoa. Andre just told me something X-TREMELY interesting. I KNEW IT!!!

Mood = Grrrrr

Will Tori get her revenge?

That night, Tori glumly surveyed the **disgusting** mess in the school theatre. Sighing, she got started scraping off a huge **glob** of dried macaroni cheese stuck on the wall. Derrick laughed at her from his post at the door, but Tori ignored him and scraped harder.

Ew, gross!

Suddenly, a voice behind her said, "I don't get it."

Tori turned around. It was Jade.

"I know Andre told you I faked the blood and the black eye," Jade said sharply. "Why didn't you tell on me?"

Tori paused. "Cos I don't want to be **fighting** all the time."

Jade looked as if her brain hurt from the **confusion**. "You can't be nice to me when I've been mean to you. That's not how it works!"

"Then try being **nice** to me sometime. Maybe that'll work." Tori held up her scraper and said, "Now go play. I've got work to do." She turned back to the macaroni cheese as she heard Jade walk away.

A minute later, an infectious dance beat **blasted** through the speakers. Surprised, Tori looked round and saw Jade picking up a scraper.

An unexpected visit

"This'll be more fun with some tunes," Jade smiled.

With the music **pumping**, Tori and Jade couldn't help dancing as they scraped away at the dried food. They even convinced Derrick to get a scraper and join in. As he got serious with his **scraping-stroke-bootyshaking**, the girls quietly danced towards the exit. As they shut the door behind them, they heard Derrick shout, *"HEY!"*

Jade whispered "Come on!" and started running away, with Tori close behind. The two girls giggled **wildly** as they ran, and Tori couldn't help thinking, *maybe this week wasn't a total loss, after all!*

The End

What Will Make You Shine?

Start
You'd rather know the gossip than be it!

That's not me!

Would you rather watch a concert or be in it?

Be in it!

For sure!

Watch it!

You hear your favourite song! Do you sing along at the top of your voice or hum the harmonies?

Sing along!

A hairbrush can also be ...

A microphone!

Hum the harmonies!

A guitar!

Talking too much!

Answer it!

Your phone rings. Answer it or let it ring?

You get told off at school for ...

Let it ring - your ringtone rocks!

Drumming your fingers on the desk.

24

Singer

You were born to entertain. Your voice is your instrument and you know how to rock it!

Tori

At parties, you love to ...

Rock the karaoke machine!

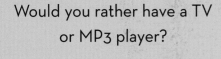

Catch up with all your friends!

Actor

Drama, drama, drama! You're not afraid to be the centre of attention. It's all about YOU!

Jade

Would you rather have a TV or MP3 player?

TV!

MP3 Player!

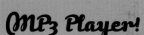

Have a good cry to your BFF.

Musician

You're perfectly OK not being in the spotlight. Playing great music is what makes you happy!

You're having a bad day. Do you ...

Write a song about it.

Andre

Costume Class with Cat

Do you have more **crazy costume flair** than Cat?
Cat is top of the class when it comes to costume design. Help her
design two costumes for her friends – the more original, the better!

The first costume is a
show-stopping outfit
for Tori's next singing
showcase – you could add
some glitter to really
Make it Shine!

The second costume is a **Halloween** costume for Jade ... so it needs to be *really scary!*

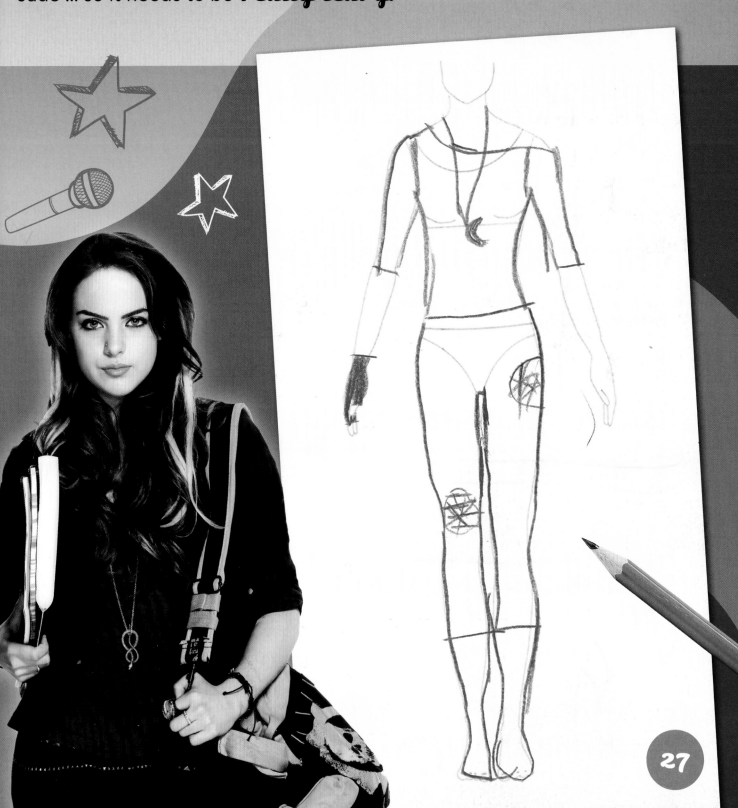

27

How Well Do You Know ...

Think you know all there is to know about *Tori* and her fellow *Hollywood Arts students?* Test your knowledge with our quiz!

1. When Tori first showcased at Hollywood Arts and won her place, who played the music as she sang?

Beck ☐
Andre ☑
Robbie ☐

2. Which song did Tori perform as Trina's 'birthweek' gift?

Make It Shine ☐
Freak the Freak Out ☐
You're the Reason ☑

3. What was the name of Robbie's blog, which got him into trouble with his friends?

Robbie Reveals ☐
Robarazzi ☑
Shapiro Undercover ☐

4. Beck won a role in a movie with which actress?

Melinda Murray ☑
Marilyn Moore ☐
Mandy Monroe ☐

5. Who's the mystery person?

Trina ☐
Jade ☐
Cat ☑

6. Who were the two girls who challenged Jade and Cat to a karaoke-off in 'Freak the Freak Out'?

Hannah and Taylor ☐
Hayley and Tara ☑
Holly and Tania ☐

Answers on Page 68.

Victorious?

7. Andre ate loads of ice cream to win a private concert by which real-life popstar?

Rihanna ☐
Ke$ha ☑
Katy Perry ☐

8. What is the name of the lunch van at the school?

The Food Dude ☐
The Grub Truck ☑
The Munch Box ☐

9. Who had to play a sweet, cheerful farm girl for a method-acting class in 'Sleepover at Sikowitz's'?

Jade ☑
Tori ☐
Trina ☐

10. The name of the school's underground website is:

TheSlam.com ☐
TheSnap.com ☐
TheSlap.com ☑

Role Call

Can you find the names of Tori and her friends hidden in the grid? They can read forwards, backwards, down, across and diagonally!

T	M	I	S	Z	R	A	Y	T	B	R	C	F	F	T
M	O	T	Y	A	L	E	M	F	E	B	N	H	O	R
F	T	R	F	G	O	U	X	I	C	G	M	N	L	O
P	P	H	I	E	A	S	K	P	K	T	Z	M	L	B
T	R	V	G	V	T	R	N	V	O	G	C	V	T	B
T	L	N	T	A	E	N	B	C	L	W	L	R	V	I
S	N	D	R	N	H	G	R	R	I	S	E	E	D	E
E	W	S	T	I	R	X	A	T	V	T	R	N	R	S
W	T	R	V	R	G	C	T	V	E	L	N	G	S	H
E	N	D	R	T	H	R	R	S	R	J	D	N	W	A
D	H	T	S	W	D	J	R	V	L	K	C	S	B	P
A	N	D	R	E	H	A	R	R	I	S	S	T	K	I
J	A	M	I	S	R	X	T	R	V	N	L	W	Z	R
F	B	S	T	Y	F	F	B	G	D	S	T	C	A	O
B	R	R	E	N	I	T	N	E	L	A	V	T	A	C

30

- ☆ TORI VEGA
- ☆ ANDRE HARRIS
- ☆ TRINA VEGA
- ☆ BECK OLIVER

- ☆ JADE WEST
- ☆ ROBBIE SHAPIRO
- ☆ REX POWERS
- ☆ CAT VALENTINE

Hollywood Smarts

Read the clues to crack the crossword!

Across

1. Tori was born to _ _ _ _ _ _ _ (7)

4. _ _ _ _ _ _ _ _, the kooky, crazy drama teacher! (8)

5. Tori updates her status on her Pear _ _ _ (3)

Down

2. _ _ _, Robbie's puppet with a mind of his own (3)

3. _ _ _ _ _ _ _ _ _ Arts, Tori's school (9)

6. Tori's motto is: Make it _ _ _ _ _! (5)

Scrambled Songs

Unscramble these crazy song titles to reveal the real songs from the show!

 1 RUFF KARAOKE TEETH

 2 YOU REHEARSE NOT

 3 SHAKE IN TIME

a MAKE IT SHINE

b FREAK THE FREAK OUT

c YOU'RE THE REASON

Answers on Page 68.

Look Closely!

1.

There are **seven differences** between these two pictures of Tori and her friends. Can you spot them all?

2.

Tick a star each time you find a difference.

Answers on Page 68.

nickelodeon
VICTORIOUS™

Beck

nickelodeon
VICTORIOUS

Act Out!

The class!

It's time to put Sikowitz's acting classes into practice!

Act out this scene from **The Great Ping-Pong Scam** with your friends, using the script below. Take turns to play the different parts. Whoever plays Robbie can 'play' Rex, too, using a puppet or a doll, and put on a funny voice.

THE GREAT PING-PONG SCAM

Tori's friends are all behaving strangely. What are they trying to hide from her?

Scene 1: School hallway.

TORI walks into school, chewing gum and checking her phone. She sees CAT, ANDRE, ROBBIE and REX talking together.

 Tori: Oh, hey!

 Cat: Hi, Tori.

 Robbie: How's it goin'?

 Andre: 'S up?

 Tori: Well, after school, I was thinkin' we should all go hang at the Grove. Ya wanna-wanna?

Andre, Robbie and Cat: (awkwardly) Uhh … Ooh … Mmm … (They look at each other then away from Tori.)

Cat: We really can't.

Tori: How come?

Robbie: We, uh, have ping-pong practice.

Cat: (agreeing) Uh-huh.

TORI doesn't believe them.

Tori: (grinning) Shut uuuup!

Andre: It's true.

Robbie: We're all on the ping-pong team.

Cat: Me, Andre, Robbie, Beck, and Jade.

Tori: (thinks they're kidding her) There's no ping-pong team at Hollywood Arts!

Robbie: Listen, Tori, ummm, you're still kinda new here and there are some things that you just don't under—

ROBBIE sniffs the air, then sniffs at TORI's face. TORI looks slightly disgusted.

Robbie: What kinda gum are you chewing?

Tori: I dunno. Sinjin made it.

ROBBIE keeps sniffing at TORI's face.

 Robbie: (to REX) Smell her mouth.

 Rex: Sure.

REX leans over to TORI and sniffs at her face.

 Rex: Hmmm ... Smells like that trip we took to Acapulco last year.

 Robbie: Yes!

 Cat: Oooh, you have Mexican-flavoured gum?

 Tori: Mexican's not a flavour! (pause) And, look, if you guys don't wanna hang out with me then just say so — why make up a lie that you're all on some ping-pong team?

CAT, ANDRE and ROBBIE look awkward.

 Cat: (friendly, starting the conversation over again) Hey, Tori.

 Robbie: How's it goin'?

 Andre: 'Sup?

 Tori: (confused) OK, so now you're gonna pretend like we're not having the conversation we're having?

 Cat: About what?

Tori:　(annoyed) The big ping-pong team lie!

TORI walks off to her locker. Her friends follow her.

 Robbie:　If ... if ... you don't believe us, then go to the rec room.

 Cat:　You can see all the trophies we've won.

 Andre:　First place.

 Tori:　(surprised) Really?

 **Andre, Robbie and Cat:**　(speaking over each other) Uh-huh. Really. It's true. Yuh-huh.

TORI thinks for a moment.

 Tori:　OK. Then I wanna try out for the team!

CAT, ANDRÉ AND ROBBIE look even more awkward and make worried noises.

 Tori:　What?

 Robbie:　Look, if you wanna try out for the ping-pong team, then you have to talk to the team captain.

 Tori:　Fine — who's the team captain?

 Cat:　Jade.

 Tori:　(not thrilled about talking to Jade!) Ulch!

Rex: Or ... you could join my team. I call it 'Rex's All-Hot-Chick Volleyball Squad.' (laughs)

TORI takes her gum out of her mouth, sticks it to REX's nose and walks away.

 Robbie: (upset) Tori!

 Rex: Get it off my nose! Get it OFF!

END SCENE.

Stage School Surgery

Being a performer is tough and surviving stage school is never going to be easy. These are some of the main challenges you might face and some of Tori's top tips for overcoming them.

Believe in yourself!

Stage fright

It's totally normal to be nervous. You just need to channel the nerves into positive drive so you're shining – not hiding – when it's time to step into the spotlight.

• Practice makes perfect – Make sure you're word-perfect before it gets to the big night. It'll give you confidence.

• Take action – When waiting backstage, jump around – it'll distract you and burn up any nervous energy!

Upstaged

Being upstaged is frustrating, whether by a fellow cast member or a friend in day-to-day life.

• Be professional – The show must go on. Focus on performing the best you can, whatever the circumstances.

• Talk about it – The best thing you can do is be open about it. Maybe they haven't realised what they're doing!

Typecast

Ignored for the parts you really want, while always being given the same old boring roles?

• Stay positive – Lots of stars are famous for playing a certain kind of role. It may be you have the look that suits a particular character – it may be a compliment!

• Don't give up – To become a top performer, you must be persistent and dream big. That means you must try, try and try again and never give up!

Write Your Own Resumé!

All performers need a great resumé to help them land great roles!
A resumé should tell people who you are, what you can do – and what
makes you so special.

My Resumé!

Real Name: _____

Stage Name: _____

Age: _____

Hair Colour: _____

Eye Colour: _____

Stick a fab photograph of yourself here!

Songs I can sing: _____
_____

Parts I can play: _____
_____

My special skills and talents include: _____
_____

My favourite co-stars are: _____
_____

My role model is: _____

You should never lie on your resumé!
Remember when Tori wrote that her special
skills were gymnastics and karate? She got cast as
a stunt double and had to make a big, dangerous fall!

47

Star Performers!

Which of the **Hollywood Arts** gang are you? Are you **kooky** Cat, **prickly** Jade, Trina the **diva** or totally **talented** Tori? Fill in the symbol that matches your answer. Then count up your totals to reveal which of the Hollywood Arts girls you're most like!

Cat's bedroom

Your bedroom is decorated:

★ With posters of my favourite bands and singers.
♥ In rainbow colours, with tons of cuddly toys.
♦ With framed pictures of me, looking fabulous.
☾ In black, with a picture of my gorgeous boyfriend by my bed.

You're picked to play Juliet in Romeo and Juliet. Are you:

☾ ... kidding?! No way! Juliet's totally lame.
★ Pleased to be chosen and hoping I'll do a great job.
♦ Totally not surprised – that role was written for me!
♥ Disappointed – I wanted to play the rabbit.

Your friends have come over to watch a movie – what kind of film will you choose?

☾ A horror – I love to be scared out of my skin!
★ A romantic comedy – I'm a big softie!
♥ A musical – they're soooo cheerful with the singing and the pretty little umbrellas and the dancing bananas ...
♦ My home movies from when I was little – I was so cute!

You'd love to turn up at school:

- ★ In a sports car with the roof off.
- ◆ In my own private jet.
- ☾ In a long, black stretch limo.
- ♥ In a spaceship.

Hollywood Arts

You're auditioning for a talent show. What do you perform?

- ☾ A dramatic play reading.
- ★ An uplifting pop song, with my best friend on piano.
- ♥ A song-and-dance followed by a sketch followed by a juggling act.
- ◆ A monologue from my one-person show, named after me and starring me.

If you scored:

Mostly ☆s

You are Tori.
You're smart and super-talented, and your friends are very important to you.

Mostly ♡s

You are Cat.
You're totally sweet but kind of dramatic and random sometimes!

Mostly ◇s

You are Trina.
You are super-focused and nothing will get in the way of your road to stardom!

Mostly ☾s

You are Jade.
You can be kind of moody, but you're creative, loyal and you work very hard.

49

Spotlight on ... Tori

Tori has grown up in the shadow of her **starry-eyed** older sister, Trina. But Tori has talents of her own, and now she's at **Hollywood Arts**, she has the chance **to shine,** too!

Resumé: *Tori Vega*

Hair colour: Brown
Eye colour: Brown

Best friend: Andre – they became friends when Tori stood in for Trina and performed at the Hollywood Arts showcase.
Best frenemy: Jade – Jade poured a cup of coffee over Tori in her first-ever class with Sikowitz!

Likes: Performing, helping her friends bring out their own talents
Dislikes: Being ordered about by her big sister, Trina!
Talents: Singing, dancing and acting.

Fave Quote: *Make It Shine!*

Three Fun Facts about *Tori*
- Tori transferred to Hollywood Arts from Sherwood High School.
- She is half Latina and understands some Spanish – she can even sing in Spanish!
- She used to own a hamster called Kevin!

Spotlight on... Andre & Trina

Resumé: Andre Harris

Hair colour: Brown
Eye colour: Brown

Best friend: Tori
Best frenemy: Trina – she wasn't happy to be paired with him in her showcase as he was only in tenth grade then, and called him 'Andrew'.

Likes: Writing and playing his music, food and especially girls!
Dislikes: Brussels sprouts and being prevented from going on dates
Talents: Composing and playing music.

Fave Quote: *Normal's boring.*

Three Fun Facts about Andre
- Andre got a crush on Jade when they worked on a song together!
- Andre once had to dress as spaghetti to perform at a children's birthday party!
- He has never been stung by a bee.

Andre is an extremely **talented musician** who can play a lot of different instruments and can also compose his own music. He's **funny** and **charming,** and looks after his paranoid grandmother, but he sometimes suffers with nerves himself especially before he performs.

Resumé: Trina Vega

Hair colour: Brown
Eye colour: Brown

Best friend: Tori – she may squabble with her little sister but Trina loves her really.
Best frenemy: Too many to name! Trina calls the gang 'Tori's friends' rather than her own, but gets upset if she's ever left out of their fun.

Likes: Performing and being the centre of attention.
Dislikes: Being upstaged or reminded that other people have talent.
Talents: Trina is very good at letting everyone know how talented she *thinks* she is.

Fave Quote: *What's up, sistaaaaaaah?*

Three Fun Facts about Trina

- Trina is pretty awesome at karate.
- Trina saw celeb blogger Perez Hilton on a plane and sneaked away his camera so she would have to return it and Perez would have to write about her!
- Trina once had to kiss Robbie for an audition!

Trina was the **star** of the family until Tori discovered her own talents. Trina is **confident** and **independent** but can sometimes be mean to people she thinks are less talented than she is, although she could definitely do with working a little harder on her own skills!

Resumé: Jade West

Hair colour: Dark brown/black
Eye colour: Green

Best friend: Beck (her boyfriend) and Cat
Best frenemy: Trina

Likes: Beck, scissors
Dislikes: Trina, springtime (she has pollen allergies)
Talents: Acting, singing and writing – Jade has written some awesome scripts and song lyrics!

Fave Quote: *I'm not your friend!*

Three Fun Facts about Jade
- Jade has a star tattoo on the inside of her right wrist!
- She once took home a lump of fat from a hospital as a souvenir.
- Jade does not like bananas.

Jade is **dark** and **moody** and looks down on anyone who isn't part of her little group. But she can also be very **insecure,** especially where her boyfriend Beck is concerned! She does have a **soft side,** though she hates people to know about it, and is surprisingly good with little kids.

Resumé: Cat Valentine

Hair colour: Red – the exact colour of a red velvet cupcake!
Eye colour: Brown

Best friend: Jade and Tori
Best frenemy: Cat is totally sweet and has no real frenemies *or* enemies – except maybe her karaoke rivals Hayley and Tara!

Likes: Red velvet cupcakes, singing, dancing, rabbits.
Dislikes: Being yelled at.
Talents: Singing, acting, juggling, designing costumes.

Fave Quote: *Kay-kay!*

Three Fun Facts about Cat
- Cat once performed three acts in a 90-second audition!
- When the gang got stuck in Beck's van in 110-degree heat, it was Cat who rescued them.
- The coat rack in Cat's bedroom spells out 'LOL' – laugh out loud!

Cat is a real **sweetheart** and is very easily pleased – especially by food. She is **energetic** and **cheerful** most of the time, and loves to tell stories about her brother. But she is also **hypersensitive** and easily offended.

Spotlight on... Beck & Robbie

Resumé: Beck Oliver

Hair colour: Dark brown
Eye colour: Brown

Best friend: Andre
Best frenemy: After dating Jade for two years, Beck knows how to steer clear of drama. He's so laidback and down-to-earth that he gets along with everyone!

Likes: Jade, acting, coffee, football.
Dislikes: Wearing khakis, running out of hair gel, Jade's mean streak.
Talents: Acting, singing, dancing, playing the guitar.

Fave Quote: *Relax!*

Three Fun Facts about Beck
• Beck is from Canada, which Jade really dislikes.
• His first professional acting role was as 'Waiter no. 1' in a movie called Miss Fire.
• Beck won't drink water from mountain streams because it has fish wee in it!

Gorgeous, brooding **Beck** was one of the first people that Tori met at Hollywood Arts – by spilling coffee on him. Beck is **serious** about his acting career, and even has a **movie role** on his resume! He lives in a cool caravan called **Silver Streak** that's parked in his parents' driveway because it's "his roof, his rules".

Resumé: Robbie Shapiro

Hair colour: Brown
Eye colour: Brown

Best friend: Cat and Andre
Best frenemy: Rex constantly bullies and insults Robbie, but the two are totally inseparable.

Likes: mayonnaise straight from the jar, his PearPad, Cat.
Dislikes: Anytime someone calls Rex a puppet.
Talents: Acting (especially comedies), doing impressions, playing the harmonica.

Fave Quote: *Hot Beef!*

Three Fun Facts about Robbie
• Robbie wears a size 8 in women's skinny jeans.
• He trims his nose hair every day.
• His school locker is covered in baby bottle teats because they remind him of happier times.

Like lots of kids, **Robbie** is a bit **awkward** and **shy**... especially around girls. But his way of dealing with his problem is pretty unique – he carries around a cheeky puppet named **Rex Powers** who never shuts up! Robbie is an **ace ventriloquist** and can speak for Rex without ever moving his lips.

Slumber Party!

A sleepover is the perfect way to chill out. Hang out like Tori and her friends by playing these fun games!

Dress Up!

Choose a student from Hollywood Arts to be for the night. Wear clothes, make-up and accessories that reflect your character's style. Then act the part - walk, talk and behave like them! You can swap roles with a friend after a while if you like.

Guess who?

Think of a Hollywood Arts student. Your friends then take turns to ask you questions to try and discover who it is. You must only answer 'yes' or 'no' to the questions. The first one to work out who you are wins!

Consequences

Start with the first heading and write a word or two, then fold your paper backwards to hide what you wrote.

Everyone then passes their paper to the person on their left. Answer the next heading, fold your paper and pass on as before.

When you've finished all the headings, open out the pieces of paper and read the hilarious stories you've created!

Headings
1. A describing word, like 'gorgeous'
2. A male student's name
3. Another describing word, like 'ditzy'
4. A female student's name
5. Where they met
6. What he said to her
7. What she said to him
8. What the consequence was ... (describe what happened afterwards)
9. What the world said

Drive-by Acting Challenge

Professor Sikowitz uses his drive-by acting challenge to test Tori and her friends on their improvisation skills. Sikowitz sneaks up on students with a video camera and challenges them to act out a situation, giving them tricky characters to perform.

Test out your acting skills with the following challenges:

The situation: At the bride's house on the morning of her wedding
Person 1: a chatty hairdresser
Person 2: a bride having second thoughts

The situation: An upmarket restaurant
Person 1: a waiter who really needs to have a wee
Person 2: an elderly customer who has lots of questions about the menu

Sikowitz's Drive-by Alphabet Acting Challenge

Sikowitz uses this challenge when he really wants to push his students. In this challenge students must begin each line of speech with the next letter of the alphabet, starting with A and working through to Z. Try it for the situations and characters above. Warning: it's tough!

Songwriting Session

Ever tried turning your thoughts into a song? Whether you're a singer or musician, songwriting is a fantastic skill to learn. And it's a great creative outlet for your emotions, good and bad. Here are some tips to get you started:

 1. ### Get Comfortable

Find a quiet, comfortable place where you can concentrate. Songwriting doesn't always come easily, so give yourself time and space to work on it.

 2. ### Be Inspired

Anything can get your creative juices flowing – a dream, something your friends are talking about or a situation you're going through. Keep a small notebook with you to write down anything you find interesting.

 3. ### Get the Message

Decide what the mood and message of your song will be. Will it be uptempo or a ballad? Do you want it to tell a story or send a message? Whatever you decide, make sure it comes from your heart.

 4. ### Less is More

Whether you start with the melody or lyrics, keep it simple so your audience can connect with it. Your song should have depth, but that doesn't mean it has to be complex.

Learn the lingo

Songs usually consist of these standard elements:

Intro

This is the short instrumental part that begins the song.

Verse

The verses tell the story of your song; there are usually 2-3 verses in each one.

Chorus

The chorus is where the real message of your song lives. It's repeated a few times to really engage the listener.

Bridge

The bridge is a verse that's in a slightly different music style to the song, in order to give a twist or change to the listener. It usually occurs in the second half of the song.

Hook

This is the catchy part of your music that the listeners can't get out of their heads. Creating one may be the hardest part of songwriting!

Think of your three favourite songs, then try and break them down to identify the elements above. Most songs will have some, if not all, of these elements.

Now that you've learned these technical tips and creative tricks, it's time to put pen to paper! The best bit of advice that all musicians give to beginner songwriters? Write every single day, because you'll only get better and better!

Jade Dumps Beck!

Take a sneaky peek at **Tori's diary** and find out what happened when Jade made a huge mistake ...

Why do I always get caught up in stuff that isn't **my** problem? Look what happened today when Jade and Beck broke up ...

So I was checking out BuzzFinger to see what's new, when I totally **freaked**. There was this picture of Beck and Alyssa Vaughn. Together!

Alyssa Vaughn! She's **famous**. And her dad's a billionaire.

It turns out Beck and Alyssa are just friends. But I guess you're wondering ... how did Jade react when she saw the picture?

So busted!

At first, Jade was cool about it. She threw a rock at Beck, but it could have been worse.

Then Alyssa starts texting Beck. Jade totally bugs out about it and starts a big fight with him. And guess who happens to walk past when they're fighting? You've guessed it, **ME**.

So Beck's like: "Tori, Tori ... c'mere."

Um ... awkward!

And I'm like: "Uh-oh!"

Beck asks: If I was his girlfriend, would I freak out about his friendship with Alyssa too? And I was honest and said **yes**, I would.

Then, just like that, Jade did something **CRAZY**. She **broke up** with Beck!

Then this evening I hear the doorbell ring, open the door and find **Jade** standing there :-O

I'm thinking: Okaaaaaay, you don't **normally** come round to see me.

WAAAHHH!

But Jade's **crying** and saying I gotta help her get Beck back. We're not friends, so I ask her why she's coming to me for help?

And she says, "Cos I don't want anybody who's **COOL** to see me like this!"

Gee, thanks :-P

Seriously?!?!

But she starts to cry again, so I agree to help her ...

Jade wants me to talk to Beck,
so I go round to his house.
He lives in his own R.V. in his
parent's driveway. He says he
got his own roof cos his parents said if he lived
under their roof, he'd have to live by their rules.
Well, that makes sense.

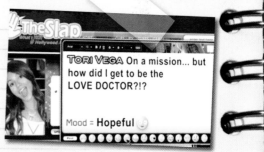

I ask him about Jade, but he says he's glad they
broke up. He can't remember the last time Jade
did something **nice** for him.

I say, what about his birthday? Cos I'm thinking
even Jade must have done something nice for his
birthday! But it turns out she just bought him
a can of **lemonade**.

No fair -
Beck's hair
is prettier
than mine!

I go back and tell Jade what Beck said. I say that she's gotta do something nice for him if she wants him back.

Jade thinks and then she gets excited. She's got an idea - she's going to get Beck a **dog**. I'm not so sure about this, but according to Jade, Beck's always wanted one.

So we go get this big, dopey doggie for Beck. It looks kinda **cute** but it's kinda **enormous**, too.

So cute! Really!

We take the dog round to Beck's R.V. Jade shoves it through the door and tells it to go lick Becks's face. Then we hear this mad barking ... along with lots of loud banging and **terrified screaming**! Suddenly, Beck turns up next to us. It's his Dad in the R.V. and the dog is **ATTACKING** him!

It all works out OK in the end. I mean, the paramedics get there quickly and say Beck's Dad shouldn't have any long-term damage. And Beck and Jade get back together! He still **loves** her and thinks the dog idea was cool anyway. And me? I got some good exercise cos Jade was too busy **making it up** with Beck to drive me home.

Can't **wait** to see what tomorrow brings :-/

Awwww.....

Make a Locker Box

Get creative and make your own ***Hollywood Arts-style*** locker box. It'll be perfect for keeping all your most precious possessions safe.

You will need:

- A cereal box
- A ruler
- Scissors
- Thick cardboard
- Glue
- Paintbrushes
- Paints
- Velcro® dots
- Stuff for decorating, like stickers, glitter pens, sparkly paper or whatever screams YOU!

1. Cut off the front of your cereal box. Then measure and cut a strip of card to make a divider and slot it inside the box about a third of the way down.

2. Measure and cut out a piece of thick cardboard large enough to wrap around the box. Score and fold it, then glue it around the sides and back of the box. Leave the front section open – this will be the locker door.

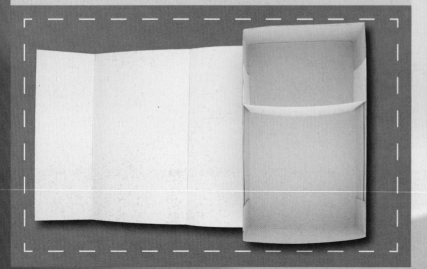

3. Paint the outside of the box a colour of your choice and leave it to dry.

4. Cut out letters and shapes from sparkly paper to decorate your locker. This design's based on Tori's locker, but you can do one that reflects your own personality!

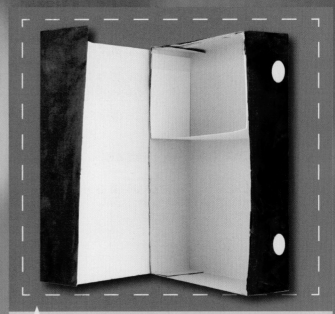

5. Stick Velcro® dots to the flap of the lid and side of the box to make the fasteners. Now pack your locker with all your favourite things!

Superstar Star Signs!

Check out what the **stars** have in store for you in the year ahead!

Aries

21 March – 19 April
The Ram

Confident and popular like Beck, you are Miss Cool. Just remember that you don't always have to be the strong one and when you're faced with a big dilemma, this year it's okay to ask for help. Your friends will be there for you when you need them.

Taurus

20 April – 20 May
The Bull

Flirty and funny like Rex, you're always the entertainer and love to make people laugh. But make sure you take time to listen, too. Someone close to you has been trying to tell you something important, but you've been too busy to hear.

Gemini

21 May – 20 June
The Twins

The twins of your star sign mean there will always be two sides to your personality. Like Robbie, you've been keeping your more adventurous side hidden recently. But no more excuses, its time to be confident, get creative and take the plunge!

Cancer

20 June –21 July
The Crab

Caring and kind like Tori, your friends really matter to you. You're always thinking about them and helping with their problems. But there will be a point this year when you need to put yourself first and take centre stage. Don't worry about upsetting people, those who really care about you will understand.

Leo

22 July – 22 August
The Lion

You know how to be a diva and keep all the attention focused on number 1, just like Trina! But this may backfire sometime this year and you'll wish you'd hadn't hogged the limelight. Don't be too hard on yourself as everyone makes mistakes. Remember to keep your sense of humour.

Virgo

23 August – 22 September
Beautiful Woman

This year is going to be lucky for you. If you have a dream then now is the time to go all out for it. Like Tori when she unexpectedly gained entrance to Hollywood Arts, this could be a year when you discover new things about yourself and get a big break you never saw coming.

Libra

23 September – 22 October
The Scales

Balanced and calm like Andre, you've been quietly plugging away at something for a long time. Now is not the time to give up! Be persistent, keep going and very soon you will get the positive recognition you deserve.

Scorpio

23 October – 21 November
The Scorpion

Passionate and independent like Jade, you're not afraid to be yourself and to speak your mind. Be careful not to make enemies of someone whose help you might need later though, as teamwork is going to be very important to you this year.

Sagittarius

22 November – 21 December
The Archer

You've been feeling a bit negative recently. But it's time to make some changes and to think about what you really want. You're going to have to be brave. Start by challenging yourself to try something new, the results may surprise you.

Capricorn

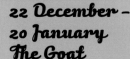

**22 December –
20 January**
The Goat

Passionate and committed, you work very hard to get what you want. But don't forget to take some time out to have some fun. Like Tori and her friends, some of the best times you'll have this year will be when you sit back, chill out and mess around with your friends.

Aquarius

21 January – 19 February
The Water Carrier

Love is in the air! If you've had a secret crush for a while, then it's definitely time to let them know. Like Beck and Jade, the course of true love may not always run smoothly for you, but it'll be worth it in the end!

Pisces

20 February – 20 March
The Fish

Like your star sign, you're as happy as a fish in water. Positive, excited and full of energy, you love trying out new things. This can mean that, like Cat, you lack focus. This year will see you faced with a big challenge and you're going to need all your willpower to see it through to the end.

Answers

p28-29:

1. Andre
2. You're the Reason
3. Robarazzi
4. Melinda Murray
5. Cat
6. Holly and Tania
7. Ke$ha
8. The Grub Truck
9. Jade
10. TheSlap.com

p30

T	M	I	S	Z	R	A	Y	T	B	R	C	F	F	T
M	O	T	Y	A	L	E	M	F	E	B	N	H	O	R
F	T	R	F	G	O	U	X	I	C	G	M	N	L	O
P	P	H	I	E	A	S	K	P	K	T	Z	M	L	B
T	R	V	G	V	T	R	N	V	O	G	C	V	T	B
T	L	N	T	A	E	N	B	C	L	W	L	R	V	E
S	N	D	R	N	H	G	R	R	I	S	E	E	D	S
S	E	W	S	T	I	R	X	A	T	V	R	N	R	V	H
W	T	R	V	R	G	C	T	V	E	L	N	G	S	A
E	N	D	R	T	H	R	R	S	R	J	D	N	W	P
D	H	T	S	W	D	J	R	V	L	K	C	S	B	I
A	N	D	R	E	H	A	R	R	I	S	S	T	K	R
J	A	M	I	S	R	X	T	R	V	N	L	W	Z	O
F	B	S	T	Y	F	F	B	G	D	S	T	C	A	J
B	R	R	E	N	I	T	N	E	L	A	V	T	A	C

p31:

Crossword:
¹PERFORM
²REX
³HOLLYWOOD
⁴SIKOWITZ
⁵PAD
⁶SHINE

p31 Scrambled Songs:

1. b
2. c
3. a

p32 Look Closely:

68